Letts

KS2
Success
Workbook

Paul Broadbent

Maths
SATs

Contents

Measures

Handling data

National Test practice and glossary

Answers

See additional answer booklet

Whole numbers

Place value

Using these three digits, make:

1 the largest possible 3-digit number

754

2 the smallest possible 3-digit number

457

3 the nearest possible number to 500

547

× and ÷ by 10 and 100

Answer the questions and complete the number puzzle.

Across

1 560 × 100

3 7032 × 10

Down

2 6800 ÷ 10

4 2400 ÷ 100

Comparing numbers

Write the correct symbol < or > in each of these.

1 7381 $>$ 7182

2 4900 $<$ 5000

3 1445 $<$ 1454

4 3769 $>$ 2992

Rounding numbers

Complete the chart by rounding to the nearest 10, 100 and 1000.

name of planet	diameter	round to the nearest 10	round to the nearest 100	round to the nearest 1000
Mercury	4878 km	4880 km	4978 km	5000 km
Earth	12 756 km	km	km	km
Mars	6794 km	km	km	km

Ordering numbers

Write this set of numbers in order, starting with the largest number.

| 4991 | 8019 | 49 325 | 8400 | HTHU 9267 |

largest

49 325

9267

8400

8019

4991

smallest

Top Tip *If you are finding numbers difficult to order, write them out one at a time in a column. Remember to line up all the units, then write them out again, starting with the largest number.*

I wish I could explore space!

So do I. You could find your own species!

Patterns and formulae

Number patterns

Write the missing numbers in these sequences.

1 31 27 _23_ 19 15 11

2 _21_ 28 35 42 49 56

3 234 236 238 _240_ 242 244

4 4 8 16 32 _64_ 128

5 1 1 2 3 5 _8_

Negative numbers

11⁻°c   *14°c*

1 What is the temperature shown on this thermometer?   _13°c_

2 What would the thermometer reading be if the
temperature dropped by 10°C?   _3°c_

3 What is the difference between −4°C and −11°C?   _7°c_

4 In Paris the temperature is 14°C, but Rome is 9°C hotter.

What is the temperature in Rome?   _23°_

*Remember to include 0°C
when looking at
temperatures.*

Top Tip

Equations

Remember, the first step to working out an equation is letters on one side,
numbers on the other.

1 50s = 200   What is the value of s?   _4_

2 6 + r = 14   What is the value of r?   _8_

3 3b + 4 = 19   What is the value of b?   _5_

Function machines

Write the answers that come out of each of these function machines.

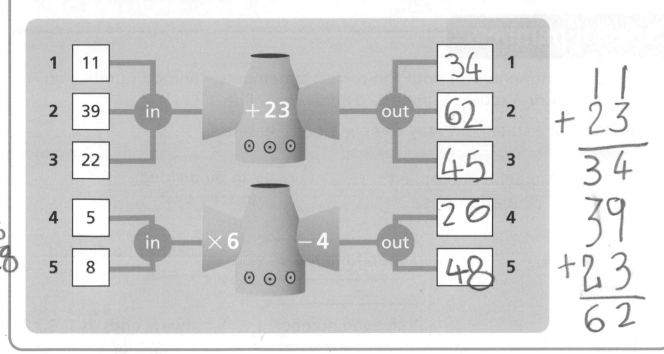

in	+23	out
1 11		34 1
2 39		62 2
3 22		45 3

in	×6	−4	out
4 5			26 4
5 8			48 5

$$\begin{array}{r} 11 \\ + 23 \\ \hline 34 \end{array}$$

$$39$$

$$\begin{array}{r} +23 \\ \hline 62 \end{array}$$

(margin notes)
×8
×6

×4
6
48

Formulae

1   In a box of 12 chocolates, *n* have toffee centres. Write a formula to show how many chocolates are not toffee centred.

      6 of Toffee

2   The price of a cinema ticket is £3. What is the price of *n* tickets?

      £1·50

That chocolate formula's hard!

Let's just eat the chocolates and find out!

Number properties

Special numbers

Complete these sentences with the correct statements – an odd number, an even number or a square number – by drawing a line.

More than one statement may complete each sentence.

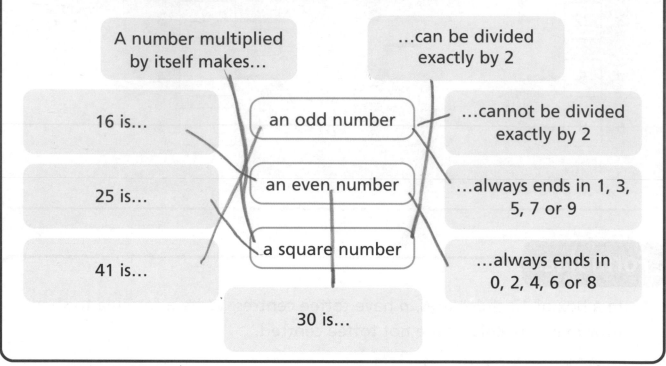

A number multiplied by itself makes…

…can be divided exactly by 2

16 is…

an odd number

…cannot be divided exactly by 2

25 is…

an even number

…always ends in 1, 3, 5, 7 or 9

41 is…

a square number

…always ends in 0, 2, 4, 6 or 8

30 is…

Sequences

Write the missing numbers in these sequences.

1 215 217 219 _221_ 223   **3** 76 74 72 _70_ 68

2 1 4 9 _16_ 25   **4** 1 3 6 _10_ 15

Top Tip Draw jumps between each number and write the differences. This will usually help you to spot the pattern.

Odd one out

Circle the odd one out in each set of numbers.

1
(92)	36
49	64
81	100

2
470	312
554	896
108	(265)

3
621	743
935	187
299	(638)

Factors

① ② 3 4 5 6 ⑦ 8 9 10

1 Underline the numbers that are factors of 36.

2 Circle the numbers that are factors of 28.

4 8 12 16 20 24 28

Multiples

1 Is 374 a multiple of 3? _____ NO

2 Which number between 102 and 108 is a multiple of 5? _____ 105

3 532 is a multiple of 4. True or false? _____ False

4 Which of these numbers does not divide exactly into 270?

2   3   4   5   6   9   2,4,5,6

Factors and multiples

Write the numbers 1–30 in the correct place on this Venn diagram.

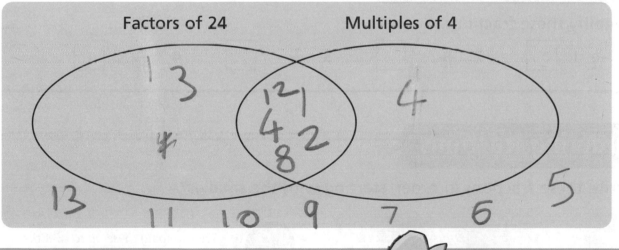

Factors of 24   Multiples of 4

1 3
12 1
4 2
8
4

13
11   10   9   7   6   5

I'm a special number – number 1!

Odd one out, you mean!

(left margin handwritten numbers)
3 6 9 2 5 8 9 20 24 8
12 16 20 24 28 32 36
7 14 21 28 35
8 46 4 32 40 a 18 27
6 12 6 8 24 30

9

Fractions

Improper fractions

Draw lines to match the improper fractions to the mixed numbers.

$\frac{16}{5}$ $\frac{5}{2}$ $\frac{5}{4}$ $\frac{14}{3}$ $\frac{7}{6}$ $\frac{11}{4}$

$1\frac{1}{6}$ $2\frac{1}{2}$ $4\frac{2}{3}$ $2\frac{3}{4}$ $3\frac{1}{5}$ $1\frac{1}{4}$

Equivalent fractions

Write the missing numbers in each of these fractions.

1 $\frac{?}{4} = \frac{3}{12}$

3 $\frac{2}{?} = \frac{14}{21}$

2 $\frac{1}{4} = \frac{5}{?}$

4 $\frac{3}{4} = \frac{?}{20}$

Simplifying fractions

Simplify these fractions.

1 $\frac{9}{12}$ **2** $\frac{6}{10}$ **3** $\frac{8}{24}$ **4** $\frac{15}{40}$

Ordering fractions

Write these fractions in order, starting with the smallest.

$\frac{2}{3}$ $\frac{5}{6}$ $\frac{1}{2}$ $\frac{5}{12}$ $\frac{3}{4}$ $\frac{7}{12}$

 Try changing these all to twelfths. They are much easier to put in order if the denominators are all the same.

smallest ⬛⬛⬛⬛⬛⬛ largest

Comparing fractions

Write the correct symbol < , > or = in each box.

$\frac{3}{5}$ ☐ $\frac{1}{2}$ $\frac{6}{12}$ ☐ $\frac{5}{6}$ $\frac{9}{10}$ ☐ $\frac{5}{7}$

Fractions of quantities

There are 18 marbles.

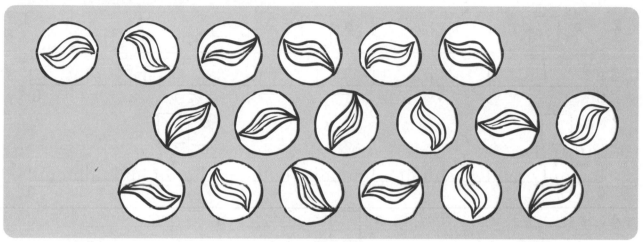

1 Colour $\frac{1}{18}$ blue.

2 Colour $\frac{1}{6}$ red.

3 Colour $\frac{4}{9}$ green.

4 Colour the rest yellow.

What fraction of the marbles are yellow? _____

I can finish this page in a fraction of the time it takes you to do it.

Yes about $\frac{10}{5}$ – that's twice as long!

Decimals

Decimal notation

Write the decimal for each arrow on these number lines.

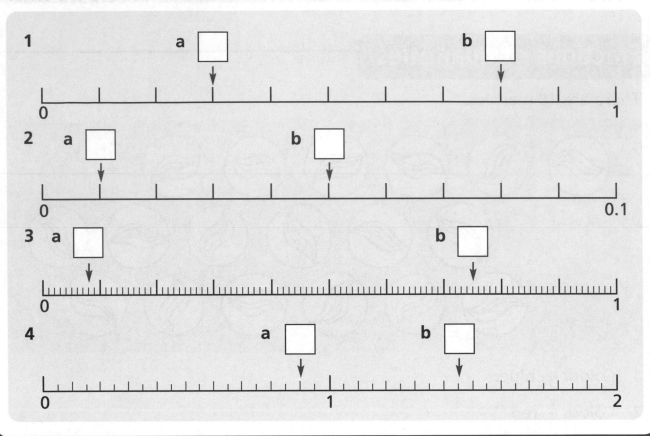

1 a ☐   b ☐

0 ———————————————————— 1

2 a ☐   b ☐

0 ———————————————————— 0.1

3 a ☐   b ☐

0 ———————————————————— 1

4 a ☐   b ☐

0 ——————————— 1 ——————————— 2

× and ÷ by 10 and 100

Choose the correct answer.

1 1.56 × 10 = ? _____

    a 0.156 **b** 15.6 **c** 156

2 13.05 × 100 = ? _____

    a 1.305 **b** 130.5 **c** 1305

3 67.24 ÷ 10 = ? _____

    a 6.724 **b** 672.4 **c** 0.6724

4 398.8 ÷ 100 = ? _____

    a 3.988 **b** 398.8 **c** 0.3988

I'm 1.52 m, which is taller than you!

But 147 cm sounds taller!

Decimals and fractions

Answer these questions.

1 Which is heavier, $3\frac{1}{2}$ kg or 3.4 kg? _____

2 What is $\frac{1}{5}$ written as a decimal? _____

3 $\frac{1}{8}$ is the same as 0.125. True or false? _____

4 Which of the decimals below is the same as $\frac{1}{100}$? _____

  1.0   0.1   0.01   0.001

Ordering decimals

Write these decimals in order, starting with the largest.

  7.05   4.6   0.98   4.56   0.02   7.43

| largest | | | | | | smallest |

Rounding decimals

Complete the chart by rounding to the nearest tenth and whole number.

	rounded to the nearest tenth	rounded to the nearest whole number
6.82	6.8	
7.105		7
0.53		

Percentages and ratio

Percentages

Answer these questions.

1 There are 30 children in a class and 20% cannot swim.

How many children cannot swim? _____

2 Rajesh got 18 out of 20 in a spelling test.

What was his score as a percentage? _____

3 There are 20 eggs in a tray and 10% of them are broken.

How many eggs are not broken? _____

4 Laura gets £2 pocket money a week. Her mum says she will increase it by 50%.

How much pocket money will she get now? _____

Money

Calculate the sale price for each of these.

1 | SALE PRICE | £_____ ○

2 | SALE PRICE | £_____ ○

3 | SALE PRICE | £_____ ○

4 | SALE PRICE | £_____ ○

5 | SALE PRICE | £_____ ○

6 | SALE PRICE | £_____ ○

Comparisons

Complete this chart.

fraction	percentage	decimal
$\frac{3}{10}$		
	25%	
		0.8

Proportion

Work out these proportions.

1   What proportion of the balloons are purple?   _____

2   What proportion of the balloons are white?   _____

3   What proportion of the balloons are long?   _____

4   What proportion of the balloons are round?   _____

Proportion is a fraction of the whole amount.

Ratio

Answer these questions.

1   Mr Hill mixes 1 pot of blue paint to every 3 pots of yellow to make green.

   If he buys 3 pots of blue, how many pots of yellow will he need? _____

2   A sandwich is made of one slice of ham to every two slices of bread.
   What is the ratio of ham to bread?   _____

3   Orange squash is diluted at a ratio of 1:5 squash to water.

   a   100 ml of squash is poured into a jug.
      How much water will be needed?   _____

   b   20 ml of squash is poured into a glass.
      How much water will be needed?   _____

Fractions investigation

Half grids

These are $\frac{1}{2}$ patterns. $\frac{1}{2}$ of each grid is coloured.

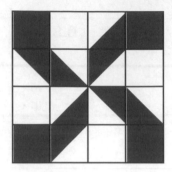 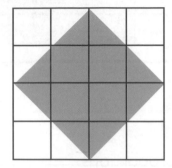

Make two patterns of your own by colouring half of each grid.

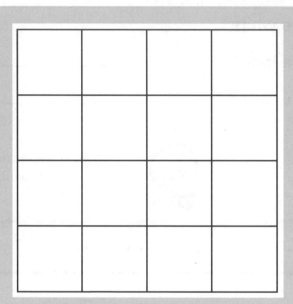 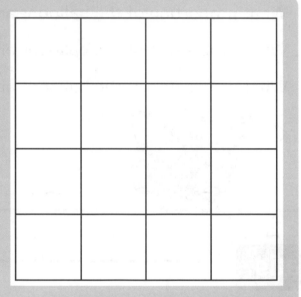

I can't get my brain around these grid patterns.

Maybe it's gridlocked!

Quarter grids

These are $\frac{1}{4}$ patterns. $\frac{1}{4}$ of each grid is coloured.

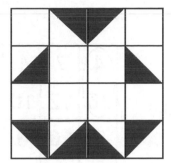 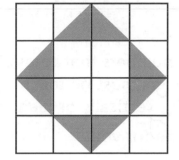

Make two patterns of your own by colouring one-quarter of each grid.

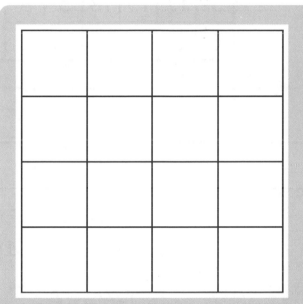 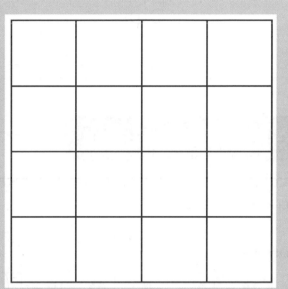

Investigate!

Investigate other fraction patterns on grids.

This one shows $\frac{5}{8}$.

Addition and subtraction

Number bonds to 20

Circle 10 pairs of numbers that total 20.
The pairs of numbers must be touching,
either horizontally, vertically or diagonally.

One has been done for you.

4	7	1	19	10	11
16	12	10	13	8	9
3	10	0	16	6	14
5	4	2	9	12	10
3	17	15	18	5	8
6	7	13	1	15	2

Mental calculations

Calculate the answers and use the code wheel
to crack the code.

You are:

34 + 16 = 50	A	91 − 19 = 72	M
53 + 19 = 72	M	78 − 28 = 50	A
27 + 23 = 50	A	54 − 9 = 45	S
32 + 9 = 41	T	63 − 22 = 41	T
46 + 45 = 91	H	82 − 77 = 5	E
17 + 28 = 45	S	65 − 49 = 16	R

Code wheel:

5 — E
91 — H
41 — T
45 — S
72 — M
72 (M) R A — 50
16 — R

Top Tip *There are lots of different mental methods. Look at each question carefully and use the best method.*

We can send messages like government agents!

I'll be 007 of course...

Written addition

Calculate the answers.

	1	2	3
	8012	5647	3390
	+ 1579	+ 3528	+ 4691
	————	————	————
	————	————	————

Use a written method to calculate these answers.

4 37.21 + 16.95 = ☐   5 2755 + 346 = ☐   6 28.09 + 4.98 = ☐

Written subtraction

Calculate the answers.

	1	2	3
	7461	9625	5330
	− 831	− 2459	− 1822
	————	————	————
	————	————	————

Use a written method to calculate these answers.

4 63.18 − 45.02 = ☐   5 4829 − 764 = ☐   6 13.5 − 9.62 = ☐

Word problems

Answer these questions.

1 Meera has saved £27 and has £28 birthday money. She wants to buy a bike for £72. How much money does she still need before she can buy the bike?

2 A tourist bus travelled 147 km to London, 16 km around the sights of London and then 147 km back home. How far did the bus travel in total?

3 Tom's Gran is 84 years old. His Mum is 35 years younger than his Gran and Tom is 38 years younger than his Mum. How old is Tom?

4 A library needs a bookshelf 2.53 m long and they have two shelves, 1.48 m and 1.7 m in length. How much will have to be cut off one of the shelves to make them fit?

Multiplication and division

Multiplication and division facts

Answer these as quickly as possible.

1 $5 \times 6 =$ 30

2 $3 \times 9 =$ 27

3 $4 \times 4 =$ 16

4 $8 \times 7 =$ 56

5 $9 \times 6 =$ 54

6 $45 \div 9 =$ 5

7 $32 \div 4 =$ 8

8 $21 \div 7 =$ 3

9 $36 \div 6 =$ 6

10 $48 \div 8 =$ 9

Multiplication grid

Complete this multiplication grid.

Top Tip
Remember, the inverse or opposite of multiplication is division. If you are stuck on a division, use multiplication to help you.

×	7	4	9
8	56	32	72
7	7	49	28	63
5	35	20	45

Written multiplication

Use a written method to answer the clues to this puzzle.

Across

2 26×18

4 37×27

5 54×13

6 86×4

Down

1 8×72

2 17×29

3 23×38

7 34×14

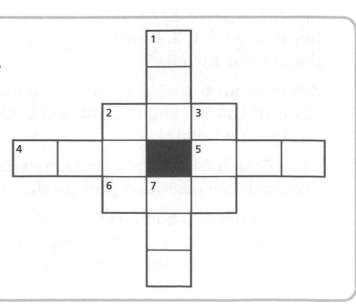

Written division

Calculate the answers.

1 ☐
8 | 912

2 ☐
9 | 306

3 ☐
4 | 908

Calculate the answers and the remainders.

4 ☐ ☐
9 | 654

5 ☐ ☐
3 | 830

6 ☐ ☐
6 | 758

Word problems

Holly is having a party. She needs enough food for 24 people. Calculate how many packs of each will be needed so that every guest has one of each item.

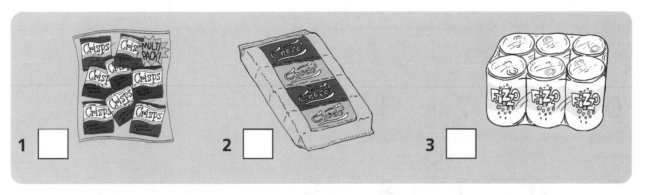

1 ☐   **2** ☐   **3** ☐

4 Five classes are going on a school trip and there are 27 children in each class. Each bus holds 45 children. How many buses will be needed? _____

5 The area of a garden is 33 m by 28 m. Grass turf is sold in loads of an area of 50 m². How many loads of turf will be needed so there is enough grass for the whole garden? _____

Missing digits investigation

1, 2 and 3

The digits 1, 2 and 3 are missing from each calculation.

Write the completed calculations.

```
    4 1 . 3 6            9 7 . 0 1
 +  4 6 . 9 2         -  5   .   7
 ─────────────        ─────────────
    9 0 . 0 8            4 5 . 7 6
```

All the digits

0	1	2	3	4
5	6	7	8	9

Choose from the digits 0–9, using each digit only once.

Make an answer as close as you can to 99.66.

```
     □ □ . □ □
 +   □ □ . □ □
   ────────────
     □ □ . □ □
```

Now try this. Make an answer as close as you can to 66.99.

```
     □ □ . □ □
 -   □ □ . □ □
   ────────────
     □ □ . □ □
```

Dividing

Use these digits to make three divisions that have answers greater than 30.

□□□ ÷ □□ = □

□□□ ÷ □□ = □

□□□ ÷ □□ = □

Multiplying

Use these digit cards.

Arrange the digits to make different pairs of 2 and 3 digit numbers.
For example, 21 and 453.

Multiply the pairs of numbers together.

Which is the largest total you can make? _____

Which is the smallest total you can make? _____

Which is the nearest number to 10 000 you can make? _____

2-D and 3-D shapes

Properties of 2-D shapes

Write the answers in the crossword to find the hidden word. The hidden word describes all of the answers to the clues!

1 a shape with 7 straight sides

2 a shape with 4 equal-length sides, opposite sides parallel, but no right angles

3 a 3-sided shape

4 a shape with 8 straight sides

5 a 6-sided shape

6 a 5-sided shape

7 a shape with 4 equal-length sides and 4 right angles

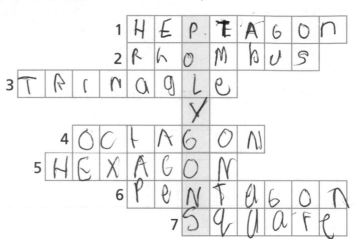

1 H E P T A G O N
2 R h o M b u s
3 T R i n a g l e
  Y
4 O C t A G O N
5 H E X A G O N
6 P e N t a g o n
7 S q u a r e

Naming 2-D shapes

Name each of these triangles.

1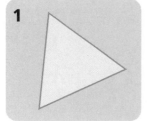

2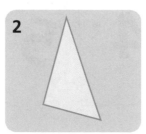

3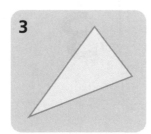

4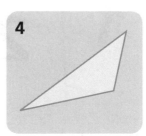

_____ _____ _____ _____

Name each of these quadrilaterals.

5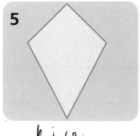

6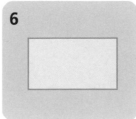

7

8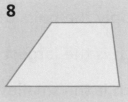

kite   rectangle   _____ _____

Symmetry

Draw all the lines of symmetry on each of these shapes.

Remember, not all shapes are symmetrical.

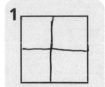 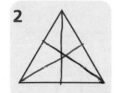 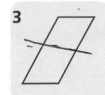 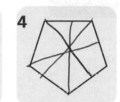

Top Tip If a shape is symmetrical, both halves are a mirror image of each other.

Naming 3-D shapes

Draw a line to join each shape to its correct name.

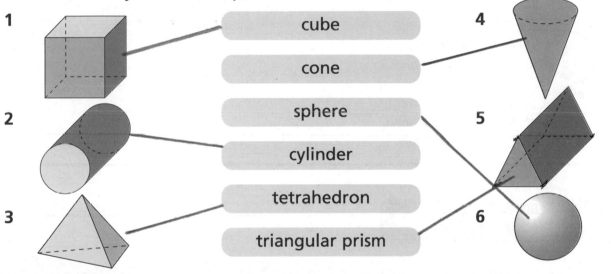

1

cube

cone

sphere

cylinder

tetrahedron

triangular prism

4

5

6

2

3

Properties of 3-D shapes

Complete this chart.

name of shape	number of edges	number of faces	number of corners
cuboid	12		
triangular prism		5	
square-based pyramid			5
tetrahedron	6		

Angles and coordinates

Plotting coordinates

Plot these coordinates.

point **a** (3, 2)

point **b** (1, 4)

point **c** (−2, 2)

point **d** (−3, −1)

Look carefully at the 4 sections of these grids. Try to learn which sections have negative numbers to describe positions.

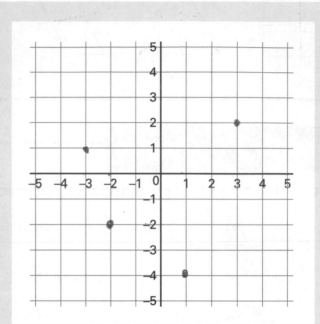

Reading coordinates

Write the coordinates for each point.

1 point a (⬚ , ⬚)

2 point b (⬚ , ⬚)

3 point c (⬚ , ⬚)

4 point d (⬚ , ⬚)

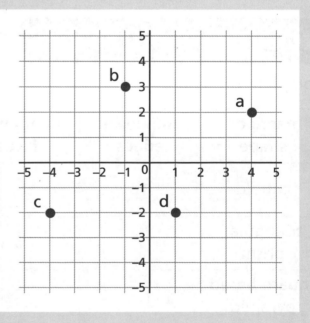

Angle facts

1 What size is a right angle? _____

2 An acute angle is less than 90°. True or false? _____

3 If two angles of a triangle are each 35°,
   what is the size of the third angle? _____

4 What is the total of all 4 angles of a rectangle? _____

Naming angles

What are each of these angles: acute, obtuse or reflex?

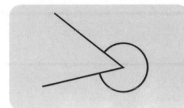   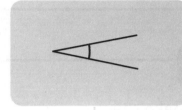   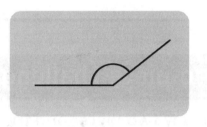

1 _reflex_   2 _acute_   3 _obtuse_

Calculating angles

Calculate the size of these angles.

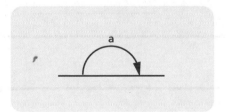

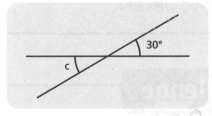

1 angle a = _180°_   3 angle c = _150°_

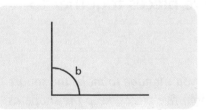

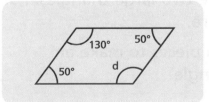

2 angle b = _90°_   4 angle d = _130°_

Tangrams investigation

What is a tangram?

This is a tangram square created over 4000 years ago in China.

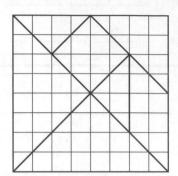

Copy this tangram carefully onto squared paper.

Stick it onto thin card and then cut out the pieces.

Note down the area of each of the seven pieces.

Mix up the pieces and try to put them back together as a square.

Two-piece challenge

Use any two pieces and try to make shapes.

1   Can you make two different triangles?
    What is the area of each triangle?   _____

2   Can you make two different squares?
    What is the area of each square?   _____

3   How many different quadrilaterals can you
    make from two pieces?   _____

Shape challenge

Try these two challenges.

• Leave out the two large triangles. Put the other five pieces together to make a square.

• Use all seven pieces to make an
  isosceles triangle.

If you manage to make the square from five pieces, keep the shape as it is and then add the two triangles to make a large isosceles triangle.

Letts

KS2 Success

Workbook Answer Booklet

Maths
SATs

Answers

Numbers

PAGES 4–5 WHOLE NUMBERS

Place value

1 754   **2** 457   **3** 475

× and ÷ by 10 and 100

¹5	²6	0	0	0
	8			
³7	0	3	⁴2	0
			4	

Comparing numbers

1 7381 > 7182   **3** 1445 < 1454

2 4900 < 5000   **4** 3769 > 2992

Rounding numbers

name of planet	diameter	round to the nearest 10	round to the nearest 100	round to the nearest 1000
Mercury	4878 km	**4880 km**	**4900 km**	**5000 km**
Earth	12 756 km	**12 760 km**	**12 800 km**	**13 000 km**
Mars	6794 km	**6790 km**	**6800 km**	**7000 km**

Ordering numbers

49 325
  9267
  8400
  8019
  4991

PAGES 6–7 PATTERNS AND FORMULAE

Number patterns

1 23   **4** 64

2 21   **5** 8

3 240

Negative numbers

1 12°C   **2** 2°C   **3** 7°C   **4** 23°C

Equations

1 4   **2** 8   **3** 5   **4** 10

Function machines

1 34   **4** 26

2 62   **5** 44

3 45

Formulae

1 12 − *n*   **2** £3*n*

PAGES 8–9 NUMBER PROPERTIES

Special numbers

A number multiplied by itself makes ➔ a square number

16 is ➔ an even number, a square number

25 is ➔ an odd number, a square number

41 is ➔ an odd number

30 is ➔ an even number

an even number ➔ can be divided exactly by 2

an odd number ➔ cannot be divided exactly by 2

an odd number ➔ always ends in 1, 3, 5, 7 or 9

an even number ➔ always ends in 0, 2, 4, 6 or 8

Sequences

1 221   **2** 16   **3** 70   **4** 10

Odd one out

circles drawn round:

1 **92** because it is not a square number

2 **265** because it is an odd number

3 **638** because it is an even number

Factors

1 underlined: 1, 2, 3, 4, 6, 9

2 circled: 1, 2, 4, 7

Multiples

1 no   **2** 105   **3** true   **4** 4

Factors and multiples

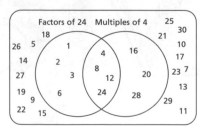

PAGES 10–11 FRACTIONS
Improper fractions

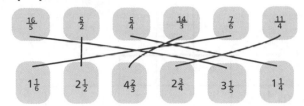

Equivalent fractions

1 $\frac{1}{4}$ **2** $\frac{5}{20}$ **3** $\frac{2}{3}$ **4** $\frac{15}{20}$

Simplifying fractions

1 $\frac{3}{4}$ **2** $\frac{3}{5}$ **3** $\frac{1}{3}$ **4** $\frac{3}{8}$

Ordering fractions

$\frac{5}{12}$ $\frac{1}{2}$ $\frac{7}{12}$ $\frac{2}{3}$ $\frac{3}{4}$ $\frac{5}{6}$

Comparing fractions

$\frac{3}{5} > \frac{1}{2}$ $= \frac{6}{12} <$ $\frac{5}{6} < \frac{9}{10} > \frac{5}{7}$

Fractions of quantities

1 1 blue   **3** 8 green

2 3 red   **4** 6 yellow; $\frac{1}{3}$

PAGES 12–13 DECIMALS
Decimal notation

1 **a** 0.3   **b** 0.8

2 **a** 0.01   **b** 0.05

3 **a** 0.08   **b** 0.75

4 **a** 0.9   **b** 1.45

× and ÷ by 10 and 100

1 b   **3** a

2 c   **4** a

Decimals and fractions

1 $3\frac{1}{2}$ kg   **2** 0.2   **3** true   **4** 0.01

Ordering decimals

7.43   7.05   4.6   4.56   0.98   0.02

Rounding decimals

	rounded to the nearest tenth	rounded to the nearest whole number
6.82	6.8	**7**
7.105	**7.1**	7
0.53	**0.5**	**1**

PAGES 14–15 PERCENTAGES AND RATIO
Percentages

1 6   **2** 90%   **3** 18   **4** £3

Money

1 £8.10   **2** £108   **3** £1.35

4 £2.10   **5** £105   **6** £12

Comparisons

fraction	percentage	decimal
$\frac{3}{10}$	**30%**	**0.3**
$\frac{1}{4}$	25%	**0.25**
$\frac{4}{5}$	**80%**	0.8

Proportion

1 $\frac{2}{3}$ **2** $\frac{1}{3}$ **3** $\frac{1}{4}$ **4** $\frac{3}{4}$

Ratio

1 9

2 1:2

3 **a** 500 ml   **b** 100 ml

PAGES 16–17 FRACTIONS INVESTIGATION
Check fraction patterns on grids.

Number facts and calculations

PAGES 18–19 ADDITION AND SUBTRACTION
Number bonds to 20
circled pairs:

4 + 16	12 + 8
1 + 19	2 + 18
11 + 9	5 + 15
10 + 10	3 + 17
6 + 14	7 + 13

Mental calculations

(34 + 16 = 50 A)	91 − 19 = 72 M
53 + 19 = 72 M	78 − 28 = 50 A
27 + 23 = 50 A	54 − 9 = 45 S
32 + 9 = 41 T	63 − 22 = 41 T
46 + 45 = 91 H	82 − 77 − 5 E
17 + 28 = 45 S	65 − 49 = 16 R

Written addition

1 9591 **2** 9175 **3** 8081

4 54.16 **5** 3101 **6** 33.07

Written subtraction

1 6630 **2** 7166 **3** 3508

4 18.16 **5** 4065 **6** 3.88

Word problems

1 £17 **2** 310 km **3** 11 **4** 0.65 m

PAGES 20–21 MULTIPLICATION AND DIVISION

Multiplication and division facts

1 30 **6** 5

2 27 **7** 8

3 16 **8** 3

4 56 **9** 6

5 54 **10** 6

Multiplication grid

×	7	4	9
8	56	32	72
7	49	28	63
5	35	20	45

Written multiplication

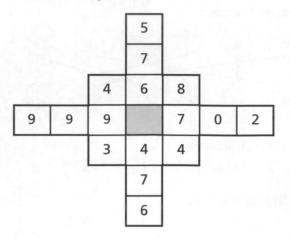

Written division

1 114 **2** 34 **3** 227

4 72 r 6 **5** 276 r 2 **6** 126 r 2

Word problems

1 3 **4** 3

2 6 **5** 19

3 4

PAGES 22–23 MISSING DIGITS INVESTIGATION

1, 2 and 3

$$
\begin{array}{r} 43.16 \\ + 46.92 \\ \hline 90.08 \end{array}
\qquad
\begin{array}{r} 97.03 \\ - 51.27 \\ \hline 45.76 \end{array}
$$

All the digits

Check child's answers.

Dividing

Check child's answers.

Multiplying

Check child's answers.

Shapes

PAGES 24–25 2-D AND 3-D SHAPES

Properties of 2-D shapes

```
    H E P T A G O N
      R H O M B U S
T R I A N G L E
          Y
      O C T A G O N
    H E X A G O N
        P E N T A G O N
          S Q U A R E
```

Naming 2-D shapes

1 equilateral triangle

2 right-angled triangle

3 isosceles triangle

4 scalene triangle

5 kite

6 rectangle

7 parallelogram

8 trapezium

Symmetry

1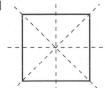

3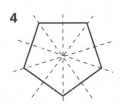

2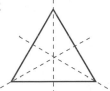

4

Naming 3-D shapes

1 cube

2 cylinder

3 tetrahedron

4 cone

5 triangular prism

6 sphere

Properties of 3-D shapes

name of shape	number of edges	number of faces	number of corners
cuboid	12	6	8
triangular prism	9	5	6
square-based pyramid	8	5	5
tetrahedron	6	4	4

PAGES 26–27 ANGLES AND COORDINATES

Plotting coordinates

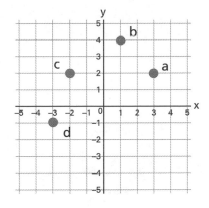

Reading coordinates

1 point a (4, 2)

2 point b (–1, 3)

3 point c (–4, –2)

4 point d (1, –2)

Angle facts

1 90°　　**2** true　　**3** 110°　　**4** 360°

Naming angles

1 reflex angle

2 acute angle

3 obtuse angle

Calculating angles

1 angle a = 180°

2 angle b = 90°

3 angle c = 30°

4 angle d = 130°

PAGES 28–29 TANGRAMS INVESTIGATION

Check child's answers.

Measures

PAGES 30–31 MEASURES

Equivalent measures

64 mm → 6.4 cm　　5600 ml → 5.6 litres

560 cm → 5.6 m　　6400 g → 6.4 kg

3900 m → 3.9 km　　3900 kg → 3.9 tonnes

Units of measures

1 kilograms (kg)

2 litres (l)

3 millilitres (ml)

4 grams (g)

Calculating amounts

1 6825 mm

2 25 litres

3 330 g

4 1.5 kg

5 2.5 litres

6 469 cm

Reading scales

1 3.9 cm　**2** 375 ml　**3** 2.5 kg　**4** 420 g

Word problems

1 856 km

2 one 2-litre bottle

3 173 cm

4 440 ml

5 1 kg

PAGES 32–33 TIME

Time facts

1 14 days = 1 fortnight

2 1 minute = 60 seconds

3 12 months = 1 year

4 60 minutes = 1 hour

5 24 hours = 1 day

6 365 days = 1 year (not a leap year)

Months and seasons

1 October

2 31

3 autumn

4 61

5 winter

Reading analogue clocks

1

3

2

4 7:30   5 3:15   6 8:50

Reading digital clocks

1 10:30

2 02:20

3 07:55

4 quarter past 6 am

5 quarter to 9 pm

6 20 to 12 am

24-hour time

1330 → 1.30 pm

0600 → 6.00 am

0130 → 1.30 am

2130 → 9.30 pm

1600 → 4.00 pm

0800 → 8.00 am

Calculating time

1 5.25 pm   3 90 minutes

2 30 minutes   4 12.20 pm

PAGES 34–35 AREA AND PERIMETER

Perimeters

1 38 cm   2 46 cm   3 44 cm

Perimeter problems

1 54 cm   2 28 cm   3 240 cm

Areas 1

1 15 cm^2 2 16 cm^2 3 20 cm^2

Areas 2

1 270 cm^2 2 36 cm^2 3 120 cm^2

Area problems

1 160 cm^2 2 5 cm   3 21 m^2

Area and perimeter

1 perimeter: 136 m   area: 960 m^2

2 perimeter: 54 m   area: 144 m^2

3 perimeter: 44 m   area: 56 m^2

PAGES 36–37 AREA INVESTIGATION

Total area of the patio is 27 square metres.

Check child's designs and answers.

Handling data

PAGES 38–39 PROBABILITY AND AVERAGES

Chance

1 1 in 2   2 1 in 6   3 1 in 3   4 1 in 4

Probability

1 1 in 2   2 1 in 4   3 1 in 6   4 1 in 12

5 1 in 3

Averages

1 6 hours   2 6 hours   3 7 hours

More averages

1 19   2 17.5   3 17

Even more averages

1 115 g   2 115 g   3 116 g

PAGES 40–41 CHARTS AND GRAPHS

Bar charts

1 18   2 3   3 46

Pie charts

1 tomato soup   3 mushroom soup

2 8

Pictograms

1 4   3 blackbird

2 7   4 6

Line graphs

1 5 cm   3 weeks 5 and 6

2 35 cm   4 55 cm

PAGES 42–43 PROBABILITY INVESTIGATION

Check child's results.

National Test practice

PAGES 44–50 TEST 1

1

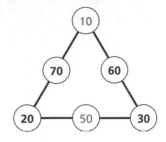

2 16p

3 a $3 \times 40 =$ **120**

   b **36** $+ 35 = 71$

   c $90 - 24 =$ **66**

4 a 90p

   b £2.30

   c cone

5 Shape C has reflective symmetry.

   Shape D is a trapezium.

   Shape A has two pairs of parallel lines.

6 6

7 1974

8 $\frac{1}{4}$

9 0.89   1.9   2.09   2.3   2.8

10 7

11 The area of the triangle should be 6 cm^2.

12 −3, −7

13 12.2 kg

14 $\frac{1}{16}$, 16

15 2.9 m

   2.97 m

   1.75 m

16 162   117

17 $\frac{6}{9}$ $\frac{2}{8}$

18 50°

19 0.36

20 perimeter: 14 cm

   area: 12.25 cm^2

PAGES 50–54 TEST 2

1 4852

2 39 cm

3 £1.14

4 4.09 pm

5 20

6 18, 19, 20

7 14.55 litres

8 0.6 litres or 600 ml

9 12p

10 90

11 9

12 8

13 £102.40

14 386 377 368 **359** 350 341 **332**

15 7.835

16

	quadrilateral	not a quadrilateral
shape with right angles		
not a shape with right angles		

17 $\frac{12}{10}$

18 85%

19

20 3 ice-creams and 5 lollies

Letts Educational
4 Grosvenor Place
London
SW1X 7DL
School enquiries: 01539 564910
Parent & student enquiries: 01539 564913
E-mail: mail@lettsed.co.uk
Website: www.letts-educational.com

First published 2007

Editorial and design: 2ibooks [publishing solutions] Cambridge

Colour Reprographics by PDQ

Author: Paul Broadbent
Book concept and development: Helen Jacobs, Publishing Director
Project editor: Lily Morgan
Illustrators: Piers Baker and Pumpkin House
Cover design: Angela English

British Library Cataloging in Publication Data. A CIP record of this book is available from the British Library.

9781843157502

Making pictures

Make pictures using all seven tangram pieces.

Here are some dancing Chinese characters!

Try making these and then design some of your own.

4000 years old? That's ancient!

Yes, it's even older than Gran!

Measures

Equivalent measures

Draw a line to join equivalent measures.

| 64 mm | 560 cm | 3.9 tonnes | 6.4 kg | 3.9 km | 5.6 litres |

| 5600 ml | 3900 m | 6400 g | 6.4 cm | 3900 kg | 5.6 m |

Units of measures

Write the correct unit for each of these.

1 4 _____ potatoes

2 2 _____ milk

3 330 _____ lemonade

4 25 _____ crisps

Calculating amounts

Answer these questions.

1 6370 mm + 455 mm = _____

2 15.8 litres + 9.2 litres = _____

3 289 g + 41 g = _____

4 What is 500 g less than 2 kg? _____

5 What is 600 ml added to 1.9 litres? _____

6 What is the total length of 3.4 m, 120 cm and 90 mm? _____

Reading scales

Write each of these measures.

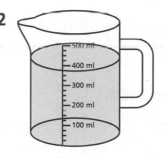

1 _____   2 _____   3 _____   4 _____

Word problems

Solve these word problems.

1   A lorry travelled 460 km from Dover to York and a further 396 km
    from York to Perth. How far did the lorry travel in total?   _____

2   Which is the largest amount: 6 cans of 330 ml or one
    2-litre bottle?   _____

3   Mr West bought a piece of wood 168 cm long, but it is
    50 mm too short. What length of wood does he need?   _____

4   Two 280 ml glasses are filled from a full one-litre carton of
    orange juice. How much orange juice is left in the carton?   _____

5   Emma has been sent to the shop to buy a 2 lb (pound) bag of sugar.
    When she gets to the shop she has these choices:

    Which one is nearest to 2 lb?   _____

Time

Time facts

Complete the missing time facts.

1 _____ days = 1 fortnight

2 1 minute = _____ seconds

3 _____ months = 1 year

4 60 minutes = 1 _____

5 _____ hours = 1 day

6 _____ days = 1 year (not a leap year)

Months and seasons

1 Which month is before November? _____

2 How many days are there in March? _____

3 Which season comes after summer? _____

4 How many days in total are there in May and June? _____

5 In which season is December? _____

Reading analogue clocks

Draw the times on these clock faces.

1 quarter to 6

2 10 past 9

3 25 past 4

Write the times shown on these clocks.

4 _____

5 _____

6 _____

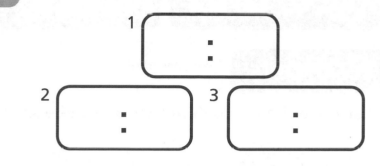

Reading digital clocks

Write the times on these clocks.
Each time is in the morning.

1 half past 10

2 20 past 2

3 5 to 8

Write the times shown on these 24-hour clocks. Use am or pm.

4 _____

5 _____

6 _____

4 06:15

5 20:45 **6** 11:40

24-hour time

Join pairs that show the same time.

| 8.00 am | 0600 | 2130 | 4.00 pm | 6.00 am | 1.30 pm |

| 1330 | 0130 | 1600 | 1.30 am | 9.30 pm | 0800 |

Calculating time

Solve these word problems.

1 It took Ross 40 minutes to do his homework. He started at 4.45 pm.
What time did he finish? _____

2 A train leaves London at 1335 and arrives at Luton at 1405.
How long was the train journey? _____

3 In a recipe it says cook the cake for $1\frac{1}{2}$ hours. The timer can only be set in
minutes. How many minutes should the timer be set for? _____

4 Beth's swimming lesson starts at 11.30 am and lasts for 50 minutes.
What time does the swimming lesson end? _____

Area and perimeter

Perimeters

Calculate the perimeter of each of these shapes.

1

8 cm

11 cm   11 cm

8 cm

_____ cm

2

14 cm

9 cm   9 cm

14 cm

_____ cm

3

7 cm

4 cm

5 cm   10 cm

6 cm

12 cm

_____ cm

Perimeter problems

Solve these word problems.

1 The sides of a rectangle measure 15 cm and 12 cm.
What is the perimeter?   _____

2 The length of one side of a square is 7 cm.
What is the perimeter of this square?   _____

3 Mrs North wants to sew lace round the edge of her
pillowcase. The pillowcase is 76 cm by 44 cm.
What length of lace will she need?   _____

Areas 1

Find the area of each shape.

1

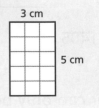

3 cm

5 cm

_____ cm²

2

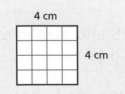

4 cm

4 cm

_____ cm²

3

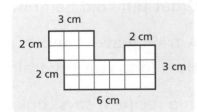

3 cm

2 cm   2 cm

2 cm   3 cm

6 cm

_____ cm²

Areas 2

Find the area of each of these shapes.

1
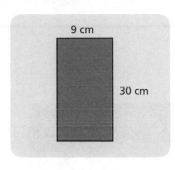
9 cm
30 cm

_____ cm²

2
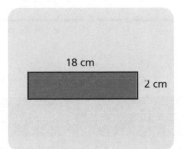
18 cm
2 cm

_____ cm²

3
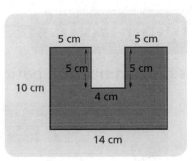
5 cm   5 cm
5 cm   5 cm
10 cm
4 cm
14 cm

_____ cm²

Area problems

Solve these word problems.

1 A rectangle is 16 cm wide and 10 cm long.
What is the area of this rectangle? _____

2 The area of a square is 25 cm².
What is the length of the sides of this square? _____

3 Mr East wants a new carpet for a room that is 4.2 m by 5 m.
How many square metres of carpet will Mr East need? _____

Area and perimeter

Calculate the area and perimeter for each of these shapes.

1
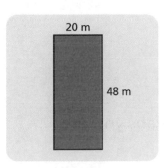
20 m
48 m

2
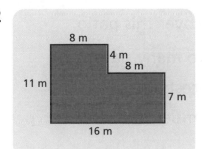
8 m
4 m
8 m
11 m
7 m
16 m

3
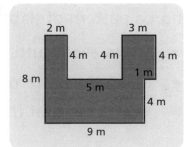
2 m   3 m
4 m 4 m   4 m
1 m
8 m
5 m
9 m
4 m

perimeter (m)

_____   _____   _____

area (m²)

_____   _____   _____

Area investigation

Patio patterns

This garden needs a patio.

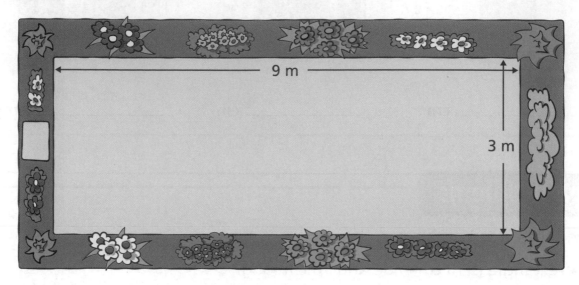

Here are the choices of paving slabs that could be used.

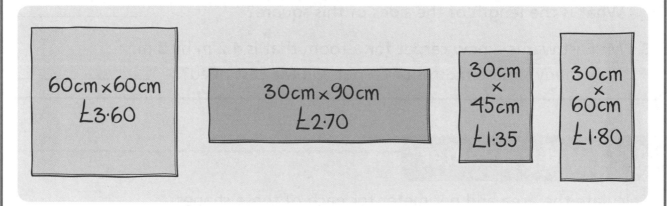

60cm × 60cm
£3·60

30cm × 90cm
£2·70

30cm × 45cm
£1·35

30cm × 60cm
£1·80

Design a pattern of slabs to cover this patio.

- Try to avoid cutting too many slabs.
- Make the pattern interesting.
- Keep a total of the number of different types of slabs you use.

What is the total area of the patio? _____

What is the total cost for all the paving slabs used
in your design? _____

What is the cost of the paving slabs per square metre? _____

Challenge

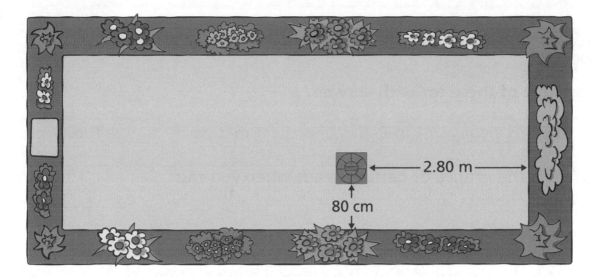

There is a manhole cover on the patio area.

- It is 50 cm × 50 cm.

- It is 80 cm from the front of the patio.

- It is 2.80 metres from the right-hand side.

Design a patio using as many whole slabs as possible.

What is the total cost for all the paving slabs used in your design?

Compare this with the design with no manhole cover.

Let's build a forest at the end of the garden.

You're out of your tree!

Probability and averages

Chance

Choose one of these for each answer.

| 1 in 6 | 1 in 2 | 1 in 3 | 1 in 4 |

1   What is the chance of getting heads when you toss a coin?   _____

2   What is the chance of throwing a four on a dice?   _____

3   What is the chance of throwing either a one or a two on a dice?   _____

4   If you toss two coins, what is the chance of them both landing on heads?   _____

Probability

The Lucky Dip at the school fete has 12 prizes left:

6 yo-yos   3 bouncy balls   2 calculators   1 mini-football

What is the probability of picking out the following?

1   a yo-yo   _____

2   a bouncy ball   _____

3   a calculator   _____

4   a mini-football   _____

5   either a bouncy ball or a mini-football   _____

What's the chance of my getting 10 out of 10 in the spelling test?

That's nothing to do with chance. It depends how much you've practised them.

Averages

This chart shows the hours of sunshine each day for one week in August.

For the hours of sunshine:

1 What is the mode? _____

2 What is the median? _____

3 What is the mean? _____

day	hours of sunshine
Monday	9
Tuesday	6
Wednesday	6
Thursday	5
Friday	7
Saturday	6
Sunday	10

More averages

Below are the spelling test scores for a group of children.

name	Jo	Amy	Sue	Ben	Josh	Lucy	Kim	Ryan
score out of 20	19	17	18	17	13	14	19	19

For this set of scores:

1 What is the mode? _____

2 What is the median? _____

3 What is the mean? _____

Top Tip '$\frac{1}{2}$', 'even chance', '50:50' and '1 in 2' all mean the same thing.

Even more averages

For these apples:

1 What is the mode? _____

2 What is the median? _____

3 What is the mean? _____

Charts and graphs

Bar charts

Look at the bar chart and answer these questions.

1   How many children have dark brown eyes?

_____

2   How many more children have green eyes than grey eyes?

_____

3   How many children took part in the survey?

_____

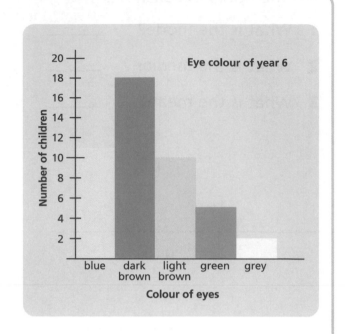

Pie charts

This pie chart shows the favourite soup of 32 people.

1   Which is the most popular soup?

_____

2   How many people preferred chicken soup?

_____

3   Which soup did 4 people choose as their favourite?

_____

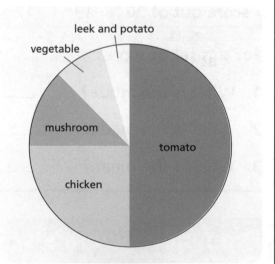

This isn't a pie chart – it's a soup chart!

Let's hope it's not a 'leak' soup chart!

Pictograms

Look at this pictogram and answer these questions.

type of bird	number of birds (🐦 = 2 birds, 🐦 = 1 bird)
sparrow	🐦 🐦 🐦
blackbird	🐦
robin	
blue tit	🐦
pigeon	🐦 🐦

1   How many pigeons visited the bird table? _____

2   How many sparrows visited the bird table? _____

3   What type of bird visited the bird table 3 times? _____

4   How many more sparrows than robins visited
    the bird table? _____

Line graphs

Look at the line graph and answer these questions.

1   How tall was the bean after 1 week?

    _____

2   How much did the bean grow
    between weeks 3 and 4?

    _____

3   Between which two weeks was
    there no change in height?

    _____

4   How tall was the bean after 6 weeks?

    _____

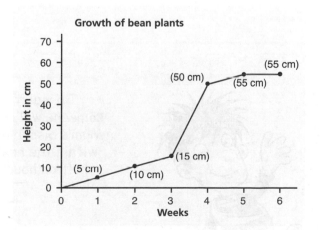

Growth of bean plants

(55 cm)
(50 cm)   (55 cm)
(15 cm)
(5 cm)   (10 cm)

Height in cm

Weeks

Top Tip   *Look carefully at the title
and the information
given on each graph
before you start to answer
the questions.*

Probability investigation

Coin toss investigation

If you toss a coin 50 times, how many times do you think it will land:

1 heads up?

2 tails up?

Now test your idea.

Toss a coin 50 times and record each outcome on this table.

outcome	tally	total
heads		
tails		

Do the results agree with your probabilities?

Repeat the experiment and compare the results.

outcome	tally	total
heads		
tails		

Top Tip

A tally is a good way of keeping a total. Remember to show sets of 5.

I predict someone will raid Mum's biscuit tin within the next half an hour!

Not if I predict it first!

Spinners investigation

- Cut out a card square and draw in the diagonals.

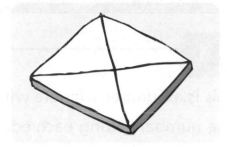

- Colour the quarters in a pattern of your choice. Make sure each quarter is one colour.

- Put a pencil through the centre to make a spinner.

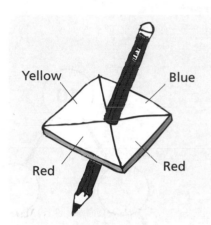

Yellow   Blue

Red   Red

- Predict the probability of landing on each of the colours on your spinner.

  For example, for this spinner the probabilities are:

  red: 1 in 2

  blue: 1 in 4

  yellow: 1 in 4

- Spin the spinner 100 times, recording the outcomes.

outcome	tally	total
yellow		
red		
blue		
green		

- Do the results agree with your predictions?

- Repeat the experiment with different spinners.

National Test practice

1 This is a number triangle with some numbers missing.

The numbers along each edge must add up to 100.

Put all the numbers 20, 30, 60 and 70 in the circles to make the totals correct.

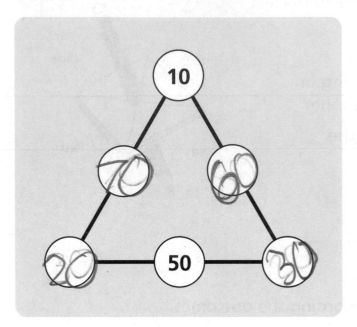

2 A stamp costs 34p.

What change will be given from 50p? _____ 16p

3 Write in the missing numbers.

a $3 \times 40 = \boxed{120}$

b $\boxed{36} + 35 = 71$

c $90 - 24 = \boxed{66}$

4   Here is the cost of ice cream.

	small	large	extra-large
cone	65p	£1.00	£1.30
choc-cone	85p	£1.20	£1.50
tub	70p	£1.05	£1.35
choc flake 15p			
raspberry sauce 10p			

a   Sam orders a small cone with choc flake and sauce.
    What is the total cost?    90

b   Alice buys two extra-large tubs of ice cream.
    What change will she get from £5?    £2.30

c   Circle the type of ice cream with the extra-large size that is double the
    price of the small.

    cone   choc-cone   tub

5 Here are four shapes.

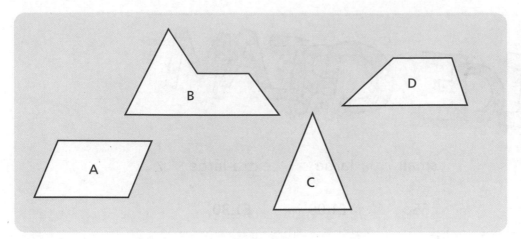

Write in the missing letters.

Shape _____ has reflective symmetry.

Shape _____ is a trapezium.

Shape _____ has two pairs of parallel lines.

6 Write in the missing number.

35 − 18 = 11 + ☐

7 Calculate 329 × 6.

Working out box

8 This bag of balls has 6 purple balls and 2 white balls in it.

A ball is taken from the bag without looking.

What is the probability that it is a white ball?

Give your answer as a fraction. _____ $\frac{1}{4}$ _____

9 Write these numbers in order of size.

| 2.8 | 2.3 | 1.9 | 0.89 | 2.09 |

0.89   1.9   2.09   2.3   2.8

smallest   biggest

10 What is the missing number?

42 ÷ ☐ 7 = 6

11 On the grid draw a triangle with the same area as the shaded rectangle. Use a ruler.

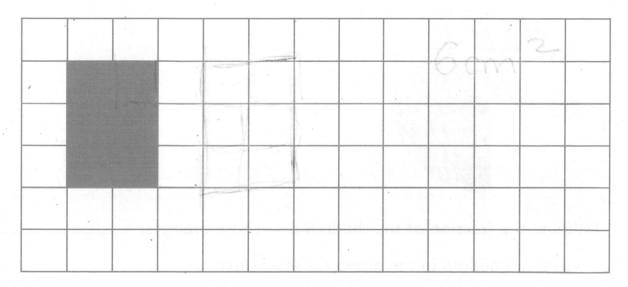

6 cm²

12 This number pattern has the rule 'subtract 4'.

Write in the missing numbers.

| 13 | 9 | 5 | 1 | -3 | -7 |

13 Three parcels weigh 34 kg altogether.

One parcel weighs 9.6 kg. The other two parcels are the same weight.

What is the weight of each of these two parcels?

Working out box

These two parcels each weigh _____

14 This pie chart shows the favourite fruit of a group of 64 children.

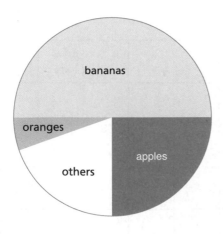

bananas

oranges

others

apples

Estimate the fraction of the children that chose oranges. _____

How many children in the group chose apples? _____

15 Five trees are planted in a field.

After two years their heights are:

| 3.8 m | 2.45 m | 2.05 m | 2.9 m | 3.65 m |

Which is the median height? _____

What is the mean (average) height of the trees? _____

What is the difference in height between the
tallest and shortest trees? _____

16 Two of these numbers divide exactly by 3. Circle the two numbers.

| 89 | 128 | 133 | 162 | 97 | 117 |

17

8   9   6   5   2

Use two of these digits to make a fraction equal to $\frac{2}{3}$ _____

Use two different digits to make a fraction equal to 0.25 _____

18 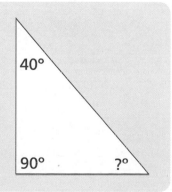 Without measuring, calculate the missing angle.

_____

40°

90°   ?°

19 What number is shown by the arrow? _____

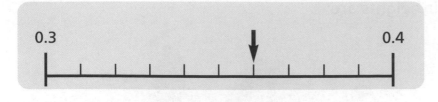

20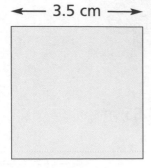

← 3.5 cm →

Calculate the perimeter of the square. _____

Calculate the area of the square. _____

Test 2

1 Use these digits to make the 4-digit number that is nearest to 5000.

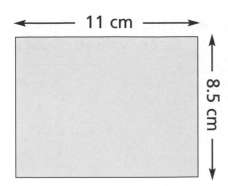

_____

2 The sides of a rectangle measure 8.5 cm and 11 cm.

← 11 cm →

8.5 cm

What is the perimeter of the rectangle? _____

3 Five identical postcards cost a total of £1.90. What is the total cost of 3 of them? _____

4 Sam arrives at a station at 3.54 pm, 15 minutes before his train is due to leave.

What is the departure time for his train? _____

5 Write in the missing number.

☐ × 18 = 360

6 The sum of three consecutive numbers is 57.

What are the three consecutive numbers? _____

A paint is mixed in the ratio of 1:3, with 1 part 'canary yellow' to every 3 parts 'emerald green'.

7 If 4.85 litres of yellow paint is used, how much green paint is needed? _____

8 The paint is put into two 10 litre tins. How much less than 20 litres is there altogether? _____

9 Hot-cross buns are 90p for 5 in a supermarket. If they are reduced in price by one-third, what is the new cost per single hot-cross bun? _____

10 Which of these numbers is not a multiple of both 3 and 4?

| 24 | 144 | 120 | 96 | 90 | 132 |

_____

11 A lift travels from the fourth floor (+4), past the ground floor (0) to the underground car park (–5).

How many floors does the lift go down? _____

12 $15 + y = 23$

What is the value of y? _____

13 A lawnmower costs £128. It is reduced in a sale by 20%.

What is the new sale price of this lawnmower? _____

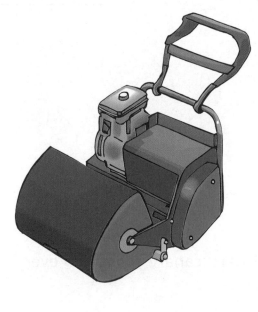

14 Write the missing numbers in this sequence.

386   377   368   _____   350   341   _____

15 $7835 \div 1000 =$ ☐

16 Draw the shapes in the correct parts of this Carroll diagram.

	quadrilateral	not a quadrilateral
shape with right angles		
not a shape with right angles		

17 Which of these fractions is equivalent to $\frac{2}{3}$?

$\frac{15}{20}$ $\qquad$ $\frac{12}{18}$ $\qquad$ $\frac{30}{40}$ $\qquad$ $\frac{16}{25}$

_____

18 In a maths test, Ali scores 17 out of 20.

What is this as a percentage? _____

19 Tick the correct net of a cube.

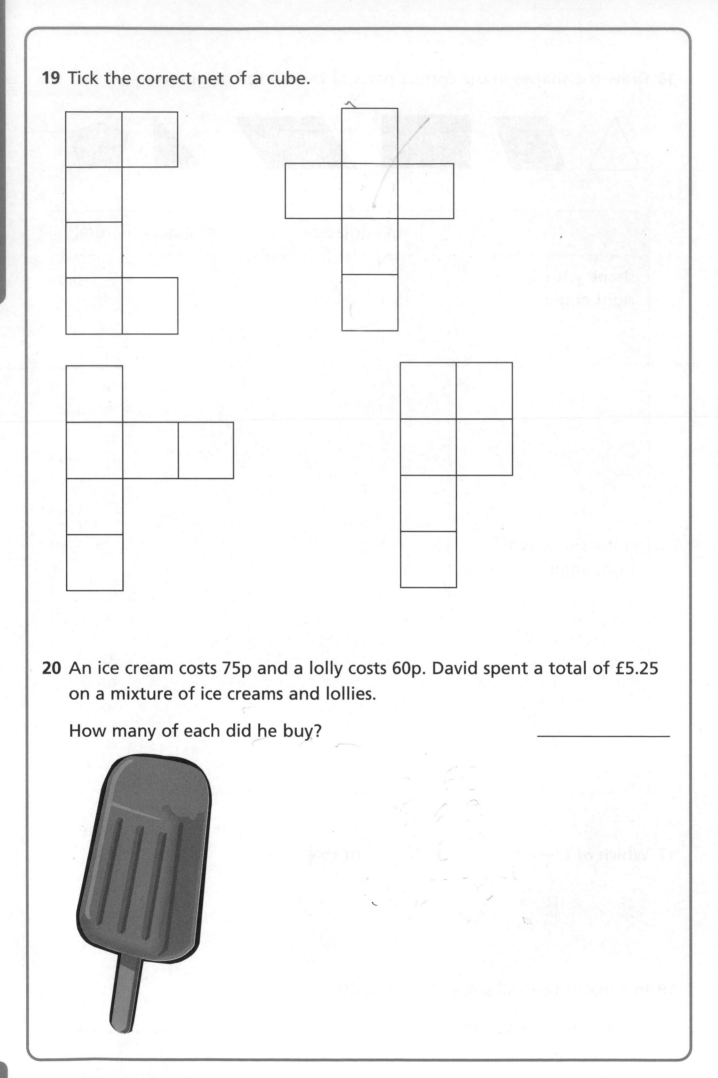

20 An ice cream costs 75p and a lolly costs 60p. David spent a total of £5.25 on a mixture of ice creams and lollies.

How many of each did he buy? _____

anti-clockwise turning in this direction, opposite to the hands of a clock.

area the area of a shape is the amount of surface that it covers.

average the middle or most common amount. There are three types of average: mode, median and mean.

axis (plural is axes) the horizontal and vertical lines on a graph.

circumference the distance all the way around the outside of a circle.

clockwise turning in this direction, like the hands of a clock.

denominator the bottom number of a fraction, the number of parts it is divided into. Example: $\frac{2}{3}$

diameter the distance right across the middle of a circle.

digit there are 10 digits: 0, 1, 2, 3, 4, 5, 6, 7, 8 and 9 that make all the numbers we use.

edge where two faces of a 3-D shape meet.

equation where symbols or letters are used instead of numbers. Example: $3y = 12$, so $y = 4$

equivalent fraction an equal fraction. Example: $\frac{1}{2} = \frac{2}{4} = \frac{3}{6}$

estimate like guessing, only using information to get a considered, approximate answer.

even number a number that can be divided exactly by 2. Even numbers end in 0, 2, 4, 6 or 8.

face the flat side of a 3-D shape.

factor a number that will divide exactly into other numbers. Example: 5 is a factor of 20

formula a formula (plural is formulae) uses letters or words to give a rule.

HTU hundreds, tens and units.

inverse opposite in effect. For example, the inverse of x is –x.

mean this is the total divided by the number of items. So the mean of 3, 1, 6 and 2 is $(3 + 1 + 6 + 2) \div 4 = 3$.

median the middle number in an ordered list. Example: 3, 8, 11, 15, 16. The median number is 11.

mode the most common number in a list. Example: 2, 6, 4, 2, 5, 5, 2. The mode is 2.

multiple a multiple is a number made by multiplying together two other numbers.

negative number a number less than zero on the number line.

net what a 3-D shape looks like when it is opened out flat.

numerator the top number of a fraction. Example: $\frac{3}{5}$

odd number a number that cannot be divided exactly by 2. Odd numbers always end in 1, 3, 5, 7 or 9.

parallel lines that are parallel never meet.

percentage this is a fraction out of 100, shown with a % sign. Example: 50% shows $\frac{50}{100}$ or $\frac{1}{2}$

perimeter the distance all the way around the edge of a shape or object.

polygon any straight-sided flat shape.

positive number a number greater than zero on the number line.

proportion this is the same as finding the fraction of the whole amount. Example: the proportion of red cubes is 3 out of 5 or $\frac{3}{5}$

radius the distance from the centre of a circle to the edge.

ratio this compares one amount with another. Example: the ratio of red cubes to blue cubes is 3:2.

sequence a list of numbers that usually has a pattern.

square number numbers multiplied by themselves make square numbers. Example: $4 \times 4 = 16$. The first five square numbers are 1, 4, 9, 16 and 25.

square roots the opposite of a square number. A number, when multiplied by itself, makes a square number, e.g. the square root of 25 is 5.

symbol a letter or sign that represents a specific quantity or function.

triangular numbers numbers made by triangle patterns. Example: $1 + 2 = 3$, $1 + 2 + 3 = 6$. The first five triangular numbers are 1, 3, 6, 10 and 15.

Venn diagram a diagram that shows groups of things by putting circles around them.

vertex (plural is vertices) this is the corner of a 3-D shape, where edges meet.